DANCING
AND SINGING
GAMES

SELECTED BY PIE CORBETT & SALLY EMERSON
ILLUSTRATED BY MOIRA & COLIN MACLEAN

Kingfisher

Kingfisher Books, Grisewood & Dempsey Ltd,
Elsley House, 24-30 Great Titchfield Street, London W1P 7AD

First published in 1992 by Kingfisher Books.
10 9 8 7 6 5 4 3 2 1
The material in this edition was previously published by Kingfisher Books in
The Kingfisher Nursery Treasury (1988), *The Kingfisher Playtime Treasury* (1989)
and *The Kingfisher Nursery Songbook* (1991).

British Library Cataloguing-in-Publication Data
A catalogue record for this book is available from the British Library

ISBN 0 86272 890 8

Phototypeset by Southern Positives and Negatives (SPAN), Lingfield, Surrey
Printed and bound in Spain

CONTENTS

Oranges and lemons,
Say the bells of St Clements.

I owe you five farthings,
Say the bells of St Martins.

When will you pay me?
Say the bells of Old Bailey.

When I grow rich,
Say the bells of Shoreditch.

When will that be?
Say the bells of Stepney.

I'm sure I don't know,
Says the great bell at Bow.

Here-comes-a-candle-to-light-you-to-bed,
Here-comes-a-chopper-to-chop-off-your-head.
Chip-chop-chip-chop-the-last-man's . . . HEAD

London Bridge is falling down,
Falling down, falling down,
London Bridge is falling down,
  My fair lady.

Build it up with iron bars,
Iron bars, iron bars,
Build it up with iron bars,
  My fair lady.

Here's a prisoner I have got,
I have got, I have got,
Here's a prisoner I have got,
  My fair lady.

You need at least six children for these two games. Two children form an arch; the others skip in a circle passing under the arch until the last lines.

For Oranges and Lemons the arch then pretends to chop the children as they pass through at CHIP and CHOP and captures one in their arms at HEAD.

The two sides of the arch are the Oranges and the Lemons, and the captive is asked to choose which he wants to be. This is done in secret so that the others don't know which side is which.

For London Bridge, a child is trapped at HERE'S A PRISONER and chooses to stand behind one of the people forming the arch.

The game is repeated until everyone has been caught. Then the two teams behind each side of the arch have a tug of war.

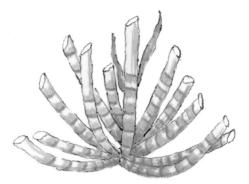

Everyone stands in a circle with one dancer in the middle.

There's a brown girl in the ring,
Tra la la la la,
There's a brown girl in the ring,
Tra la la la la,
There's a brown girl in the ring,
Tra la la la la,
For she like sugar and I like plum.

The dancer skips across the circle.

Then you skip across the ocean,
Tra la la la la,
Then you skip across the ocean,
Tra la la la la,
Then you skip across the ocean,
Tra la la la la,
For she like sugar and I like plum.

The dancer wiggles for the MOTION.

Then you show me your motion,
Tra la la la la,
Then you show me your motion,
Tra la la la la,
Then you show me your motion,
Tra la la la la,
For she like sugar and I like plum.

The dancer chooses a partner and they wheel around.

Then you wheel and take your partner,
Tra la la la la,
Then you wheel and take your partner,
Tra la la la la,
Then you wheel and take your partner,
Tra la la la la,
For she like sugar and I like plum.

Oh, we can play on the big bass drum,
    And this is the way we do it:
BOOM, BOOM, BOOM goes the big bass drum,
    And that's the way we do it.

Oh, we can play on the little flute,
    And this is the way we do it:
TOOTLE, TOOTLE, TOOT goes the little flute,
    And that's the way we do it.

Oh, we can play on the tambourine,
    And this is the way we do it:
TING, TING, TING goes the tambourine,
    And that's the way we do it.

*The song continues, changing the instrument
each time. Older children may like to
add the noise of the new instrument with
each verse until you have the whole band.*

Other verses
FIDDLE DIDDLE DEE
   goes the violin *etc*.

TICKA TICKA TECK
   go the castanets *etc*.

ZOOM ZOOM ZOOM
   goes the double bass *etc*.

TA TA TARA
   goes the bugle horn *etc*.

The big ship sails on the alley, alley O.
The alley, alley O, the alley, alley O.
The big ship sails on the alley, alley O.
On the last day of September.

At least five dancers are needed but the more the better.
Start in a line, holding hands with one dancer standing by
a wall with her hand high against the wall to make an arch (1).

The Captain said, "This will never, never do,
Never never do, never never do".
The Captain said, "This will never, never do".
On the last day of September.

Sing as the dancer at the end of the line leads
everyone through the arch (2).

10

The big ship sank to the bottom of the sea.
The bottom of the sea, the bottom of the sea.
The big ship sank to the bottom of the sea.
On the last day of September.

3

When the last player passes through the arch the player making the arch will find her arm tugged under her so that she has to twist around and face the other way with her arms crossed and held up (3).

The line now comes back round and through the arch made between the player nearest to the wall and her neighbour (4).

4

5

When the dancers have been through all the arches and all have crossed arms, they form a ring and sing the last verse – sadly (5).

We all dip our heads in the deep blue sea.
The deep blue sea, the deep blue sea.
We all dip our heads in the deep blue sea.
On the last day of September.

The Farmer's in his den,
The Farmer's in his den,
Eee-Aye-Eee-Aye,
The Farmer's in his den.

The Farmer wants a Wife,
The Farmer wants a Wife,
Eee-Aye-Eee-Aye,
The Farmer wants a Wife.

The Wife wants a Child,
The Wife wants a Child,
Eee-Aye-Eee-Aye,
The Wife wants a Child.

The Child wants a Nurse,
The Child wants a Nurse,
Eee-Aye-Eee-Aye,
The Child wants a Nurse.

The Nurse wants a Dog,
The Nurse wants a Dog,
Eee-Aye-Eee-Aye,
The Nurse wants a Dog.

The Dog wants a Bone,
The Dog wants a Bone,
Eee-Aye-Eee-Aye,
The Dog wants a Bone.

We all pat the Bone,
We all pat the Bone,
Eee Aye Eee Aye,
We all pat the Bone.

Choose someone to be the FARMER who stands in the middle of a circle. The circle holds hands and moves around clockwise while they sing. The Farmer chooses a WIFE and she joins him in the middle. She then chooses a CHILD and so on until the DOG picks someone to be the BONE. If you have lots of players – at least fourteen – the ones in the middle form a new circle that moves around in the opposite direction to the outside circle. On the last verse everyone comes in to the middle to pat the poor Bone. The only good thing about being the Bone is that you can be the next Farmer.

Rosy apple, mellow pear,
　　Bunch of roses she shall wear;
Sword and pistol by her side;
　　I know who shall be my bride.

Take her by the lily-white hand,
　　Lead her across the water,
Blow her a kiss and say goodbye,
　　For she's the Captain's daughter.

Stand in a circle holding hands and choose one dancer to stand in the middle. Everyone dances around singing the first verse. Then the dancer in the middle picks the BRIDE. These two then form an arch by holding both hands up high. The circle dancers skip under the arch for the second verse. On the last line the arch comes down capturing someone – he or she has to stand in the middle for the next game. At least five players are needed – the more, the better.

In and out the windows,
In and out the windows,
In and out the windows,
As we have done before.

Stand and face your partner,
Stand and face your partner,
Stand and face your partner,
As we have done before.

Now follow her to London,
Now follow her to London,
Now follow her to London,
As we have done before.

Bow before you leave her,
Bow before you leave her,
Bow before you leave her,
As we have done before.

*This dance requires at least six dancers who all stand in a
circle holding their hands up high to form arches between
each other. Choose one dancer to skip in and out of the arches
during the first verse. On STAND AND FACE he stops by
one of the other dancers and waits. During the third verse he
follows her in and out of the arches. For the last verse they
move to the middle of the ring and bow or curtsey to each
other. The partner becomes the next one in the middle and
the game is repeated until everyone has had a turn.*

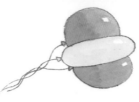

You put your right arm in,
Your right arm out,
Your right arm in,
And you shake it all about.
You do the Hokey Cokey,
And you turn around,
That's what it's all about.

Chorus

Oh, the Hokey, Cokey, Cokey!
Oh, the Hokey, Cokey, Cokey!
Oh, the Hokey, Cokey, Cokey!
Knees bend,
Arms stretch,
Ra! Ra! Ra!

Other verses
You put your left arm in *etc.*
You put your right leg in *etc.*
You put your left leg in *etc.*
You put your whole self in *etc.*

ra ra ra

ra ra ra

Any number can play but the song is more fun the more dancers there are. Everyone stands in a circle and follows the actions as they sing the verses. For the chorus everyone joins hands and dances into the middle and out three times; bends knees, stretches out arms and shouts RA RA RA!

Moonshine tonight, come mek me dance and sing,
Moonshine tonight, come mek me dance and sing;
Me deh rock so, you deh rock so,
Under banyan tree.
Me deh rock so, you deh rock so,
Under banyan tree.

Ladies may curtsey, and gentlemen may bow,
Ladies may curtsey, and gentlemen may bow;
Me deh rock so, you deh rock so,
Under banyan tree.
Me deh rock so, you deh rock so,
Under banyan tree.

Then we join hands, and dance around and round,
Then we join hands, and dance around and round;
Me deh rock so, you deh rock so,
Under banyan tree.
Me deh rock so, you deh rock so,
Under banyan tree.

Everyone joins hands and dances in a circle to the first verse;
stands and carries out the action of the second verse, then
joins hands and dances around for the last verse.

An odd number of players is needed for this game. Choose one player to stand in the ring; the others choose partners. On the first verse the player in the middle picks another and they dance together around the outside of the ring. Then they join the circle.

Lou, lou, skip to me lou,
Lou, lou, skip to me lou.
Lou, lou, skip to me lou,
　Skip to me lou, my darling.

Now the player who had her partner stolen skips around the outside of the ring.

Lost my partner, what shall I do?
Lost my partner, what shall I do?
Lost my partner, what shall I do?
　Skip to me lou, my darling.

She then chooses someone else's partner to dance around with before standing back in the ring. Then the game and the song start again.

I've found anuvver one, just like you,
I've found anuvver one, just like you,
I've found anuvver one, just like you,
　Skip to me lou, my darling.

In and out the dusty bluebells,
In and out the dusty bluebells,
In and out the dusty bluebells,
Who shall be my partner?

Tippitty tappitty on your shoulder,
Tippitty tappitty on your shoulder,
Tippitty tappitty on your shoulder,
You shall be my partner.

This is a ring dance for at least six dancers. Everyone stands in a circle holding their hands up high to make an arch between each dancer. One dancer is chosen to start the dance and during the first verse she weaves in and out of the arches. On WHO SHALL BE MY PARTNER she stops and taps whoever is closest on the shoulder for the second verse. This dancer joins onto the first dancer and they weave in and out again as the first verse is repeated.

Little Sally Waters, sitting in a saucer,
  Rise Sally, rise and dry your eyes.
Fly to the East, fly to the West,
  Fly to the one you love the best.

Now you are married, you must be good,
  And help your wife to chop the wood.
You chop it thin and bring it in,
  There's your love with a wedding ring.

*Stand in a circle and choose someone to go
in the middle. She sits down until BEST when
she gets up and chooses someone from the
circle. They both join hands and skip around
the ring together for the second verse. The one
who was chosen then goes into the middle.
Play with at least four people.*

I sent a letter to my love
And on the way I dropped it,
A little puppy picked it up
And put it in his pocket.
It isn't you, it isn't you,
  But it is you.

*Stand or sit in a circle and choose one player to
walk around the circle. On IT IS YOU he
drops the letter (any small object) behind one
of the players. That player picks it up and
races around in the opposite direction to get
back to his place before the first player reaches
it. Whoever gets there last starts the game
again.*

A ring dance for five or more players.

The wind blows low, the wind blows high,
The rain comes scattering down the sky.
She is handsome, she is pretty,
She is the girl of the golden city.
So, *Claire West* will you marry me?

If you love him clap your hands,
If you hate him stamp your feet.
The wind blows low, the wind blows high,
The stars are dropping from the sky,
Claire West thinks she'll die.
For want of the golden city.

Now *Tom Saunders* takes her by the hand,
Now he leads her to the water,
Gives her kisses one-two-three-
Mrs *West's* handsome daughter.

Stand in a ring and choose one dancer to stand in the middle. Her name goes into the last line of the first verse. Decide who she will marry and whisper it round. At the end of the second verse she can clap her hands or stamp her feet. At the start of the third verse put in the name of the dancer she will marry. They dance around together.

Do you know the Muffin Man,
The Muffin Man, the Muffin Man,
Do you know the Muffin Man,
Who lives in Drury Lane?

Yes, I know the Muffin Man,
The Muffin Man, the Muffin Man,
Yes I know the Muffin Man
Who lives in Drury Lane.

Two of us know the Muffin Man,
The Muffin Man, the Muffin Man,
Two of us know the Muffin Man
Who lives in Drury Lane.

Choose one player to stand in the middle of a ring. The ring dances around to the first verse, then the player in the centre picks someone who sings the second verse. These two join hands and dance in the middle singing the third verse.

Repeat the verses changing the number of players until everyone is dancing around singing "We all know the Muffin Man". The game is for six or more players.

Let's go to Kentucky
Let's go to the fair,
To see a senorita,
With flowers in her hair.
Shake it, shake it, shake it,
Shake it if you can;
Oh, rumble to the bottom,
Rumble to the top,
Round and round,
Round and round,
Until you cannot stop.

At least five players are needed. Choose one to be the SENORITA. Everyone else dances round her, stopping on SHAKE. The Senorita then has to SHAKE in the middle; on RUMBLE, everyone shakes. At the end the Senorita spins round and round with her eyes closed and one arm pointing. Whoever she is pointing at when she stops is the next Senorita.

THE ECHO GAME

This is a good way to learn clapping rhythm. Sit in a circle with one player in the middle. This player claps out a rhythm on his shoulder, knee or arm and everyone else must copy. Any number can play.

THE NAME GAME

Everyone sits in a circle with one player in the middle. This player claps out the rhythm for a name and if it is your rhythm you clap it back. For example:

An - war   Jes - si - ca
Clap clap   clap clap clap

WHO STOLE THE COOKIES?

All players:	Who stole the cookie from the cookie jar? Number One stole the cookie from the cookie jar.
Number One:	Who, me?
All players:	Yes, you.
Number One:	Not I.
All players:	Then who? Who stole the cookie from the cookie jar?

Number One:	Number Eight stole the cookie from the cookie jar.
Number Eight:	Who, me?
All players:	Yes, you.
Number Eight:	Not I.
All players:	Then who? Who stole the cookie from the cookie jar?
Number Eight:	Number Five stole the cookie from the cookie jar.

Up to ten players can join in this game. They sit in a circle and each picks a number for themselves – a different number from one to ten. Everyone claps their own hands and their neighbour's alternately, and chants the words.

The player who is Number One picks the number of another player. This player has to continue quickly by choosing another number – any number so long as it hasn't already been picked. If it has, the player calling the number is out.

Old Macdonald had a farm,
E-I-E-I-O.
And on that farm he had some cows,
E-I-E-I-O.
With a moo-moo here,
And a moo-moo there,
Here a moo, there a moo,
Everywhere a moo-moo,
Old Macdonald had a farm,
E-I-E-I-O.

Old Macdonald had a farm,
E-I-E-I-O.
And on that farm he had some sheep,
E-I-E-I-O.
With a baa-baa here,
And a baa-baa there,
Here a baa, there a baa,
Everywhere a baa-baa,
Old Macdonald had a farm,
E-I-E-I-O.

*Repeat the song with different animals
and noises.*

Oats and beans and barley grow,
  Oats and beans and barley grow,
But not you nor I nor anyone know,
  How oats and beans and barley grow.

First the farmer sows his seed,
  Then he stands and takes his ease,
Stamps his feet and claps his hands
  And turns around to view the land.

A-waiting for a partner,
  A-waiting for a partner,
Now open the ring and let one in,
  So oats and beans and barley grow.

Choose someone to be the FARMER in the middle of
the ring. Everyone dances around for the first verse.
Then the Farmer pretends to SOW the seed; STANDS with
his hands on his hips; STAMPS his feet, CLAPS and TURNS
around to look at his land. During the last verse he picks
a partner who becomes the next farmer.

Here we go round the mulberry bush,
The mulberry bush, the mulberry bush,
Here we go round the mulberry bush,
On a cold and frosty morning.

This is the way we wash our hands,
Wash our hands, wash our hands,
This is the way we wash our hands,
On a cold and frosty morning.

Repeat the first verse and dance in a circle after each verse.

Other verses
This is the way we wash our face *etc.*
This is the way we brush our hair *etc.*
This is the way we clean our teeth *etc.*
This is the way we put on our clothes *etc.*

Join hands and dance in a circle. Everybody falls down at the last line.

Three times round went our gallant, gallant ship,
And three times round went she;
Three times round went our gallant, gallant ship,
Till she sank to the bottom of the sea.

Still holding hands, pull each other up again.

Pull her up, pull her up, said the little sailor boy,
   Pull her up, pull her up, said he,
Pull her up, pull her up, said the little sailor boy,
   Or she'll sink to the bottom of the sea.

T here was a princess long ago,
Long ago, long ago,
There was a princess long ago,
Long, long ago.

*Choose a PRINCESS, a WICKED FAIRY
and a PRINCE. The princess stands
in the centre of the ring.*

And she lived in a big high tower,
A big high tower, a big high tower,
And she lived in a big high tower,
Long, long ago.

Raise hands to make a tower.

A wicked fairy waved her wand,
Waved her wand, waved her wand,
A wicked fairy waved her wand,
Long, long ago.

*The wicked fairy waves an
imaginary wand over the princess.*

The princess slept for a hundred years,
A hundred years, a hundred years,
The princess slept for a hundred years,
Long, long ago.

A great big forest grew around,
Grew around, grew around,
A great big forest grew around,
Long, long ago.

Wave arms like trees in the wind.

A gallant prince came riding by,
Riding by, riding by,
A gallant prince came riding by,
Long, long ago.

The prince rides around outside the circle.

He chopped the trees down one by one,
One by one, one by one,
He chopped the trees down one by one,
Long, long ago.

He pretends to chop his way through the circle.

He took the princess by the hand,
By the hand, by the hand,
He took the princess by the hand,
Long, long ago.

He takes the princess's hand and she wakes up.

So everybody's happy now,
Happy now, happy now,
So everybody's happy now,
Happy now.

The circle skips around faster and faster.

INDEX OF FIRST LINES